Share It! 2

Sharebook

Fiona Davis

CB126744

macmillan education

Table of Contents

Unit 5 **I Can Do It!** pages 27–32	**Lesson 2** Student **A** page 27 Student **B** page 29	***Can or Can't?***	Student A: *The artist can draw, but he can't fly.* Student B: *The artist can draw, but he can't fly. The teacher can write and read.*
	Lesson 5 Student **A** page 31 Student **B** page 31	***Can You Jump Rope?***	Student A: *Can you jump rope?* Student B: *Yes, I can.*
Unit 6 **My Day** pages 33–36	**Lesson 2** Student **A** page 33 Student **B** page 33	***I'm Out!***	Student A: *What do you do in the morning?* Student B: *I eat breakfast.*
	Lesson 5 Student **A** page 35 Student **B** page 36	***When?***	Student A: *Number one. When does Matt get up?* Student B: *He gets up at eight o'clock.*
Unit 7 **Playtime!** pages 37–42	**Lesson 2** Student **A** page 37 Student **B** page 37	***What Do You Like Doing?***	Student A: *Do you like playing soccer?* Student B: *Yes, I do. Do you like taking photos?*
	Lesson 5 Student **A** page 39 Student **B** page 41	***Favorite Activities***	Student A: *What does he like doing?* Student B: *He likes dancing.*
Unit 8 **Cool Clothes** pages 43–46	**Lesson 2** Student **A** page 43 Student **B** page 43	***Memory Game***	Student A: *Whose shirt is that?* Student B: *It's David's shirt. Whose sneakers are those?*
	Lesson 5 Student **A** page 45 Student **B** page 46	***What's Joey Wearing?***	Student A: *What's Joey wearing?* Student B: *He's wearing a jacket, shorts, a T-shirt, a baseball cap, and sneakers.*

Key Terms

Student A

Student B

cards

a page

face down

face up

a pile of cards

a set of cards

cut the cards

take a card

mix the cards

turn over a card

same

different

a chart

ask a question

answer a question

Memory Game

Student A

How to Play:

Students A and B: Mix the cards. If you can touch the card, ask *What's this?* If you point to the card, ask *What's that?*
Student A: Touch or point to a card. Turn it face up. Ask.
Student B: Answer. Take the card if you are correct. Turn the card face down if you are not correct.
Students A and B: Take turns. The winner is the student with the most cards.

Example:

Student A: *What's this? / What's that?*
Student B: *It's a goat.*
Student A: *Yes.*

Unit 1 Lesson 2 Memory Game

Student B

How to Play:

Students A and B: Mix the cards. If you can touch the card, ask *What's this?* If you point to the card, ask *What's that?*

Student A: Touch or point to a card. Turn it face up. Ask.

Student B: Answer. Take the card if you are correct. Turn the card face down if you are not correct.

Students A and B: Take turns. The winner is the student with the most cards.

Example:

Student A: *What's this? / What's that?*

Student B: *It's a goat.*

Student A: *Yes.*

Find the Insects!

Student A Student B

How to Play:
Students A and B: Look at the pictures. Then ask and answer questions to find the insects or animals. Take turns asking and answering questions. Color your picture.

Example:
Student A: *Number one. What are those?*
Student B: *They're bees.*
Student A: *Three bees. OK.*

Unit 2 Lesson 2 His or Her?

Student A Student B

How to Play:
Students A and B: Look at your page for one minute.
Students A and B: Look at the pictures. Take turns.
Decide if it is his item or her item. Write *his* or *her* in the correct box. Then compare with your partner.

Example:
Student A: *That's his camera.*
Student B: *No, that's her camera.*

Unit 2 Lesson 2 His or Her?

Student A Student B

How to Play:
Students A and B: Look at your page for one minute.
Students A and B: Look at the pictures. Take turns. Decide if it is his item or her item. Write *his* or *her* in the correct box. Then compare with your partner.

Example:
Student A: *That's his camera.*
Student B: *No, that's her camera.*

Unit 2 Lesson 5 My or Your?

Student A Student B

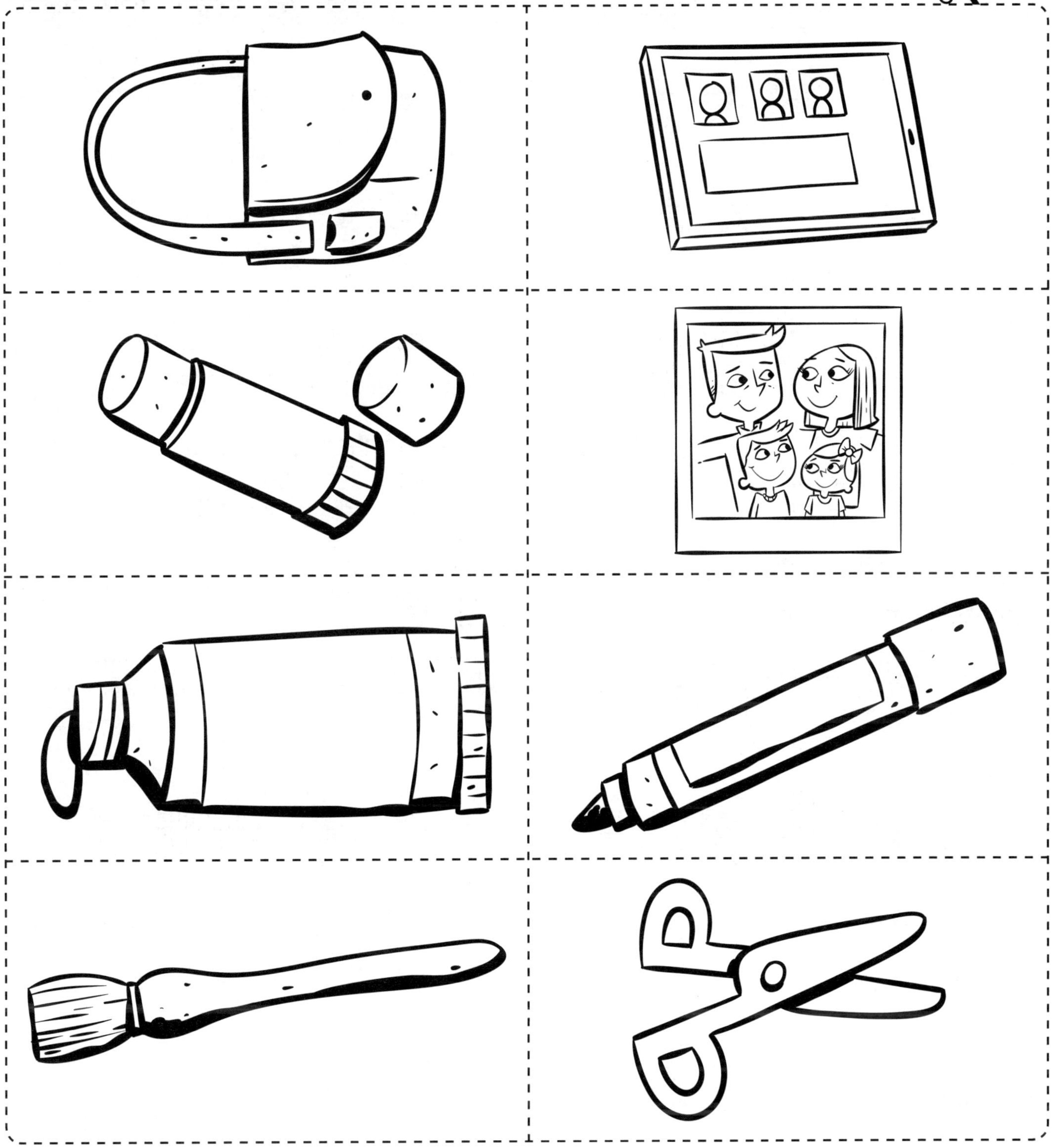

How to Play:

Students A and B: Color your cards. Then put your cards face down in front of you.
Student A: Point to one of your cards. Then ask a question.
Student B: Turn the card over and answer.
Students A and B: If no, it's Student B's turn. If yes, point to one of Student B's cards and guess. Take turns. The student with the most pairs is the winner.

Example:

Student A: *Is this my tablet?*
Student B: *Yes, it is.*
Student A: *Is that your tablet?*
Student B: *No, it isn't. My turn.*

Is There an Elephant?

Student A

Find

E = an elephant

G = giraffes

T = tigers

S = snakes

How to Play:
Students A and B: Look at your grid. Do not show your partner.
Students A and B: Take turns. Ask questions to find the missing animals. Write the number for each animal in each box.
Compare your pictures.

Example:
Student A: *Is there an elephant in Number 10?*
Student B: *No, there isn't.*
Student B: *Are there hippos in Number seven?*
Student A: *Yes, there are.*

Unit 3 Lesson 2 Is There an Elephant?

Student B

Find

M = monkey

C = a crocodile

H = hippos

Z = zebras

How to Play:
Students A and B: Look at your grid. Do not show your partner.
Students A and B: Take turns. Ask questions to find the missing animals. Write the number for each animal in each box.
Compare your pictures.

Example:
Student A: *Is there an elephant in Number 10?*
Student B: *No, there isn't.*
Student B: *Are there hippos in Number seven?*
Student A: *Yes, there are.*

Hide the Animals!

Student A Student B

Use: in / on / next to / between / in front of / behind

How to Play:
Students A and B: Hide your animals on your map.
Student B: Ask Student A to tell you where the animals are.
Put the animal game pieces in the correct places on the map.
Compare your pictures. Then change roles.

Example:
Student A: *Where's the tiger?*
Student B: *It's behind the school.*

Unit 4 Lesson 2 Find Out!

Student A Student B 

NAME:	1 ME!	2	3	4

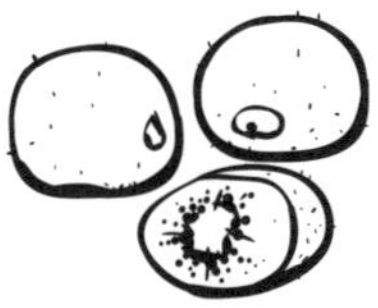				

How to Play:
Students A and B: Work with another pair. Write your names in the chart. Then complete the Me! column. Use a check (✔) or cross (✘).
Students A and B: Work together to ask, answer, and complete the information in column 2. Then change partners and complete columns 3 and 4.

Example:
Student A: *Do you like pears?*
Student B: *No, I don't.*
Student A: *Does she like pears?*
Student B: *Yes, she does!*

What Do You Want for Dinner?

Student A

How to Play:
Students A and B: Place the food cards face up in a pile.
Place the meal cards face down in a pile.
Student A: Pick a meal card. Ask Student B a question.
Student B: Choose two food cards and answer the question.
Keep the food cards. Put the meal card back in the pile.
Continue until all the cards are gone. Then change roles.

Example:
Student A: *What do you want for dinner?*
Student B: *I want a burger and pie, please.*

What Do You Want for Dinner?

Student B

How to Play:
Students A and B: Place the food cards face up in a pile.
Place the meal cards face down in a pile.
Student A: Pick a meal card. Ask Student B a question.
Student B: Choose two food cards and answer the question.
Keep the food cards. Put the meal card back in the pile.
Continue until all the cards are gone. Then change roles.

Example:
Student A: *What do you want for dinner?*
Student B: *I want a burger and pie, please.*

Unit 5 Lesson 2 Can or Can't?

Student A

artist

draw (✔) and fly (✘)

teacher

write (✔) and read (✔)

horse

jump (✔) run (✔)

dog

swim (✔) draw (✘)

bird

fly (✔) write (✘)

Jason

jump (✔) draw (✘)

butterfly

fly (✔) walk (✘)

cat

walk (✔) write (✘)

How to Play:
Students A and B: Mix all the cards. Put them face down in a pile.
Student A: Turn over one card and put it in a line. Look at the picture and read the card. Say the sentence.
Student B: Turn over another card and put it in the line. Look at the picture and read the card. Repeat Student A's sentence and add the new sentence. How many sentences can you make?

Example:
Student A: *The artist can draw, but he can't fly.*
Student B: *The artist can draw, but he can't fly. The teacher can write and read.*

Unit 5 Lesson 2 Can or Can't?

Student B

Jenny

draw (✔) fly (✘)

turtle

walk (✔) swim (✔)

spider

walk (✔) draw (✘)

children

swim (✔) run (✔)

police officer

swim (✔) jump (✔)

monkey

jump (✔) read (✘)

fish

swim (✔) walk (✘)

firefighter

walk (✔) read (✔)

How to Play:
Students A and B: Mix all the cards. Put them face down in a pile.
Student A: Turn over one card and put it in a line. Look at the picture and read the card. Say the sentence.
Student B: Turn over another card and put it in the line. Look at the picture and read the card. Repeat Student A's sentence and add the new sentence. How many sentences can you make?

Example:
Student A: *The artist can draw, but he can't fly.*
Student B: *The artist can draw, but he can't fly. The teacher can write and read.*

Unit 5 Lesson 5 Can You Jump Rope?

Student A Student B

NAME:	1 ME!	2 ______	3 ______	4 ______

How to Play:
Students A and B: Work with another pair. Write your names in the chart. Then complete the Me! column for you. Use a check (✔) or cross (✘).
Students A and B: Work together to ask, answer, and complete the information in column 2. Then change partners and complete columns 3 and 4.

Example:
Student A: *Can you jump rope?*
Student B: *Yes, I can.*
Student A: *Can she jump rope?*
Student B: *No, she can't.*

Unit 6 Lesson 2 I'm Out!

Student A Student B

morning

afternoon

evening

How to Play:
Students A and B: Color your own set of cards. Place all three of the time cards in a pile face down. Keep your other cards in your hand.
Student A: Pick up a time card. Ask Student B a question.
Student B: Use one of your cards to answer. Keep the card if you can make a sentence. Take turns. When you have no more cards, you are the winner!

Example:
Student A: *What do you do in the morning?*
Student B: *I eat breakfast.*

Unit 6 Lesson 5 When?

Student A

How to Play:
Students A and B: Take turns asking questions. Fill in the time on each picture. Then compare your pictures.

Example:
Student B: *Number one. When does Matt get up?*
Student A: *He gets up at eight o'clock.*

Unit 6 Lesson 5 When?

Student B

How to Play:
Students A and B: Take turns asking questions. Fill in the time on each picture. Then compare your pictures.

Example:
Student B: *Number one. When does Matt get up?*
Student A: *He gets up at eight o'clock.*

Unit 7 Lesson 2 What Do You Like Doing?

Student A Student B

What do you like doing?	ME	________

How to Play:
Students A and B: Look at the pictures. Complete the first column with a check (✔) or cross (✘).
Student A: Ask Student B about an activity. If Student B likes the activity, check the box (✔). If not, write an (✘).
Student B: Ask Student A about an activity. If Student A likes the activity, check the box (✔). If not, write an (✘).
Complete your charts. Count the activities you both like.

Example:
Student A: *Do you like playing soccer?*
Student B: *Yes, I do. Do you like taking photos?*

Favorite Activities

Student A

Person Cards

How to Play:
Students A and B: Place your cards face down in front of you.
Student A has Person Cards. Student B has Activity Cards.
Student A: Turn over a Person Card. Ask the question.
Student B: Turn over an Activity Card. Answer the question. If correct, keep the card. If you can't answer, turn the card face down.
Then change roles.

Example:
Student A: *What does he like doing?*
Student B: *He likes dancing.*

Favorite Activities

Student B

Activity Cards

How to Play:
Students A and B: Place your cards face down in front of you.
Student A has Person Cards. Student B has Activity Cards.
Student A: Turn over a Person Card. Ask the question.
Student B: Turn over an Activity Card. Answer the question. If correct, keep the card. If you can't answer, turn the card face down.
Then change roles.

Example:
Student A: *What does he like doing?*
Student B: *He likes dancing.*

Memory Game

Student A Student B

How to Play:
Students A and B: Look at the picture for one minute. Then look at the 12 pictures. Take turns to ask and answer questions about the clothing items. Write *D*, *E*, or *S* in each box. Then compare.

Example:
Student A: *Whose shirt is that?*
Student B: *It's David's shirt. Whose sneakers are those?*
Student A: *They're Sara's sneakers.*

Unit 8 Lesson 2

Memory Game

Student A Student B

How to Play:
Students A and B: Look at the picture for one minute. Then look at the 12 pictures. Take turns to ask and answer questions about the clothing items.
Write *D*, *E*, or *S* in each box. Then compare.

Example:
Student A: *Whose shirt is that?*
Student B: *It's David's shirt. Whose sneakers are those?*
Student A: *They're Sara's sneakers.*

What's Joey Wearing?

Student A

Find: Joey / Laurie / Michael / Tom

How to Play:
Students A and B: Ask questions to find and label the four people on your list.
Then compare your pictures.

Example:
Student A: *What's Joey wearing?*
Student B: *He's wearing a jacket, shorts, a T-shirt, a baseball cap, and sneakers.*

Unit 8 Lesson 5 What's Joey Wearing?

Student B

Find: Clare / Jake / Lisa / Ana

How to Play:
Students A and B: Ask questions to find and label the four people on your list.
Then compare your pictures.

Example:
Student A: *What's Joey wearing?*
Student B: *He's wearing a jacket, shorts, a T-shirt, a baseball cap, and sneakers.*

My Sharebook Game Log

Sharebook 2		Game	Date	Players
1	Lesson 2	Memory Game		
	Lesson 5	Find the Insects!		
2	Lesson 2	His or Her?		
	Lesson 5	My or Your?		
3	Lesson 2	Is There an Elephant?		
	Lesson 5	Hide the Animals!		
4	Lesson 2	Find Out!		
	Lesson 5	What Do You Want for Dinner?		
5	Lesson 2	Can or Can't?		
	Lesson 5	Can You Jump Rope?		
6	Lesson 2	I'm Out!		
	Lesson 5	When?		
7	Lesson 2	What Do You Like Doing?		
	Lesson 5	Favorite Activities		
8	Lesson 2	Memory Game		
	Lesson 5	What's Joey Wearing?		

I can play games in English!

Macmillan Education Limited
4 Crinan Street
London N1 9XW

Companies and representatives throughout the world

Sharebook ISBN 978-1-380-02286-8
Student Book Pack ISBN 978-1-380-02281-3

Written by Fiona Davis

The author has asserted their right to be identified as the author of this work in accordance with the Copyright, Designs and Patents Act 1988.

Share It! is a registered trademark published by Macmillan Education Limited

First published 2020

Designed by Pronk Media, Inc.
Illustrated by: Drew Pocza pp. 7, 9, 10–11, 13, 15, 17, 18, 19, 21, 23–24, 25, 27, 29, 31, 33, 35, 36-37, 39, 41–42, 43, 45, 47, 49, 51, 53; Emi Ordás & Wedoo Studio p. 47.
Cover design by Roberto Martinez, Marcin Rojek, and Wojciech Szulik
Cover Illustration by Emi Ordás

Author's acknowledgements
The author would like to thank the *Share It!* team for their support and encouragement.

Printed and bound in Brazil.
2025
65